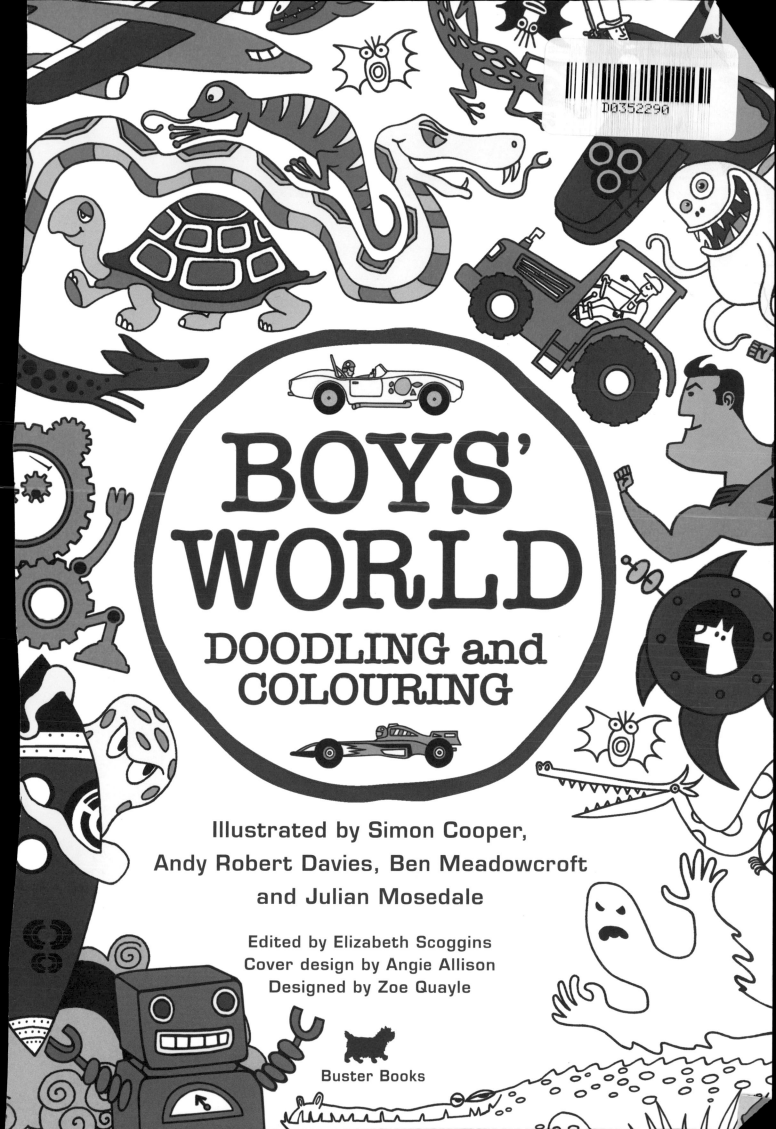

BOYS' WORLD

DOODLING and COLOURING

Illustrated by Simon Cooper,
Andy Robert Davies, Ben Meadowcroft
and Julian Mosedale

Edited by Elizabeth Scoggins
Cover design by Angie Allison
Designed by Zoe Quayle

Buster Books

It's time to get creative!

Doodle daring designs and colour with confidence, as you complete this brilliant book in your own unique way.

Whether you're drawing detail with a black pen or adding cool colours with felt-tip pens, pencils or crayons, it's up to you to add your own stamp to every picture.

If you are drawing on top of coloured areas on the pages, leave your ink to dry for a moment to avoid smudges.

Now go wild and get inspired!

First published in Great Britain in 2011 by Buster Books,
an imprint of Michael O'Mara Books Limited,
9 Lion Yard, Tremadoc Road, London SW4 7NQ, www.mombooks.com/busterbooks

A CIP catalogue record for this book is available from the British Library.

ISBN: 978-1-907151-68-2

2 4 6 8 10 9 7 5 3 1

Printed and bound in June 2011 by Tien Wah Press Ltd,
4 Pandan Crescent, Singapore, 128 475.

This book was created, completed and coloured by

....

Add more crazy monsters!

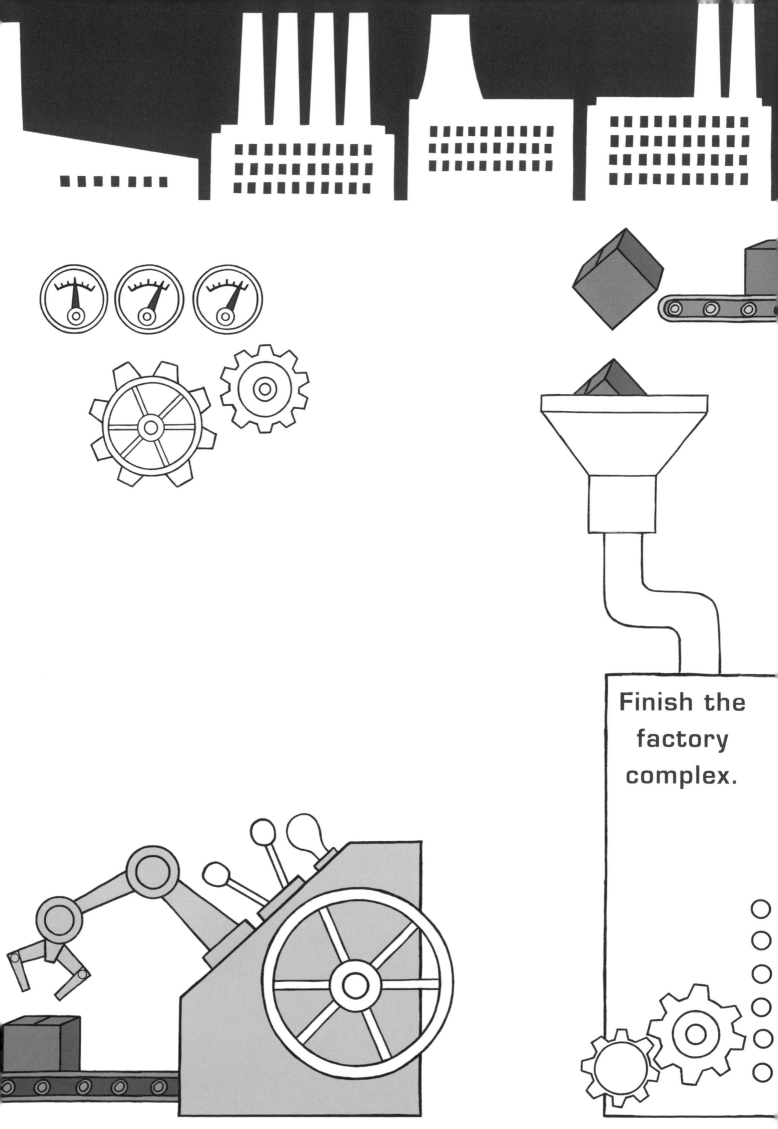

Finish the
factory
complex.

Aliens and monsters.

Make this a mad science experiment.

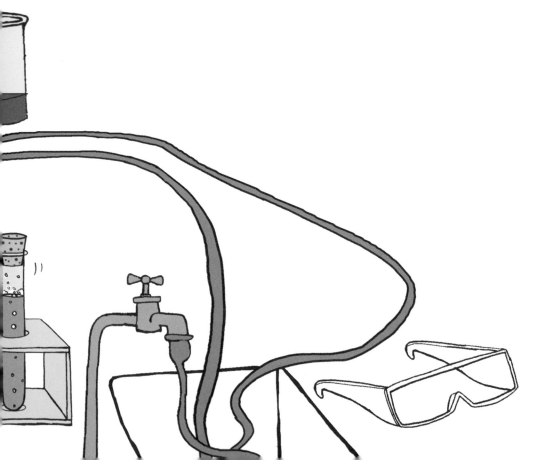

Complete this treasure map.

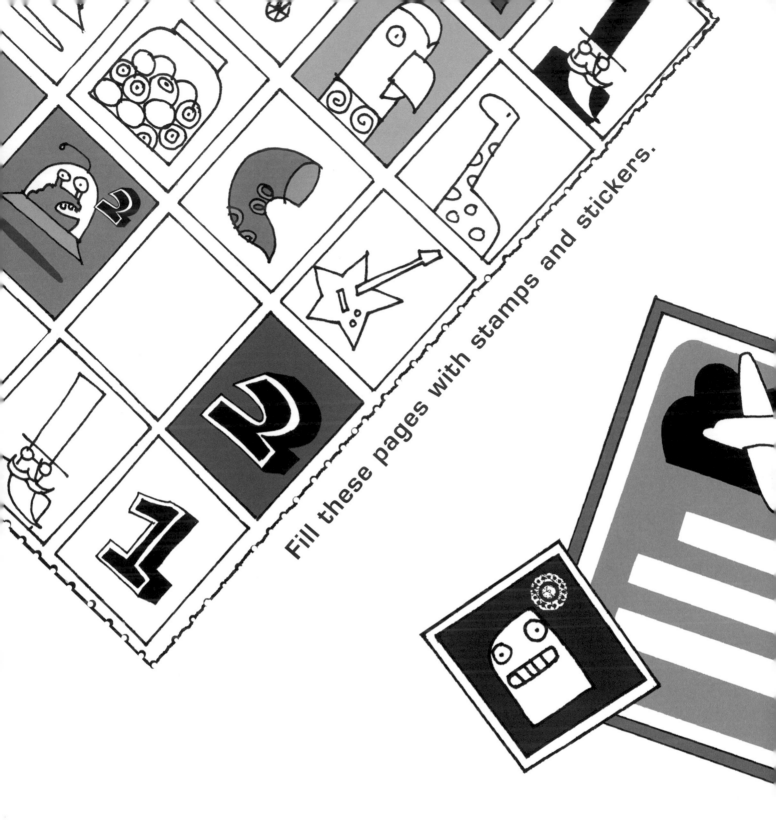

Fill these pages with stamps and stickers.

What's haunting the house?

Complete the crazy racing cars and design your own.

Fill the sea with fearsome ships
with terrifying figureheads.

Quick! Camouflage these trucks and tanks.

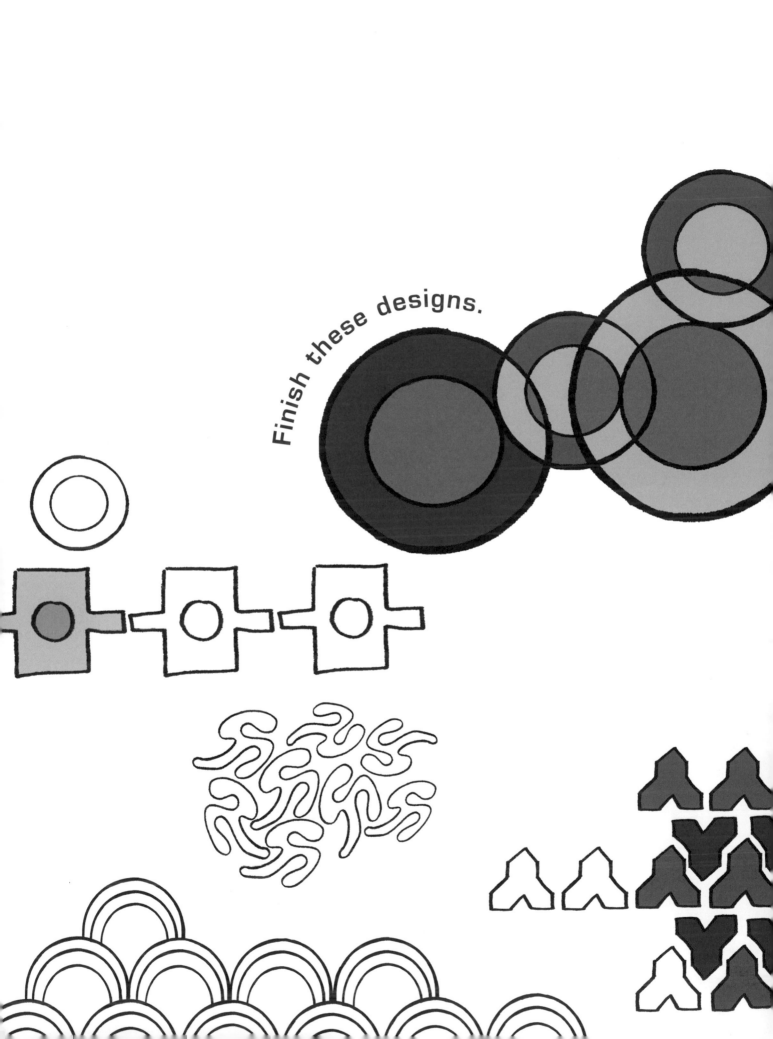

Finish these designs.

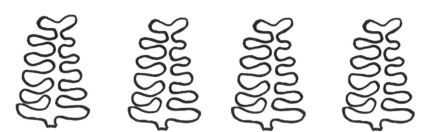

Make these sand castles really realistic.

Complete the city skyline.

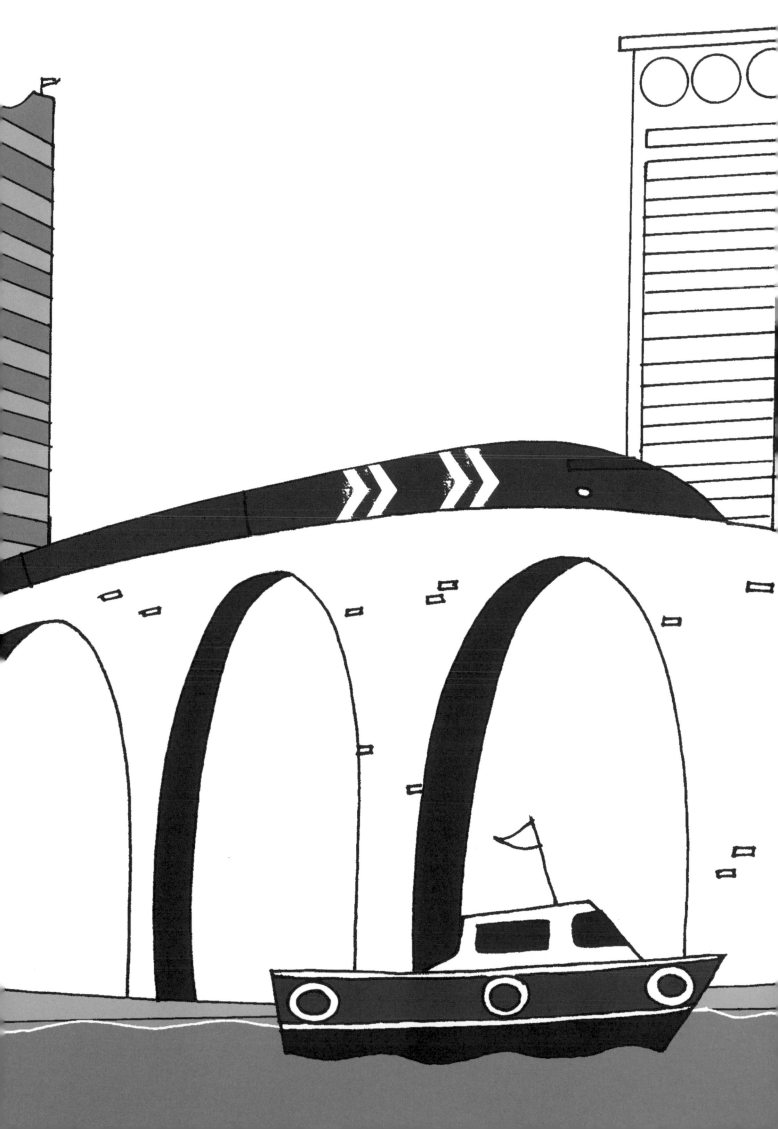

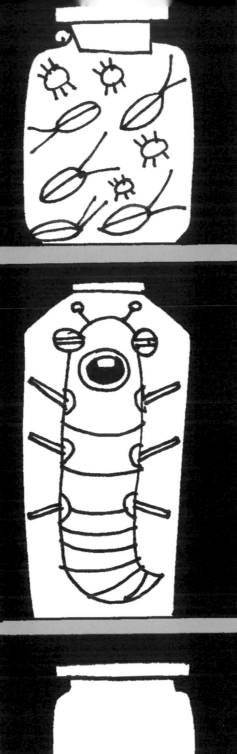

Fill the jars with gross stuff for monsters to buy.

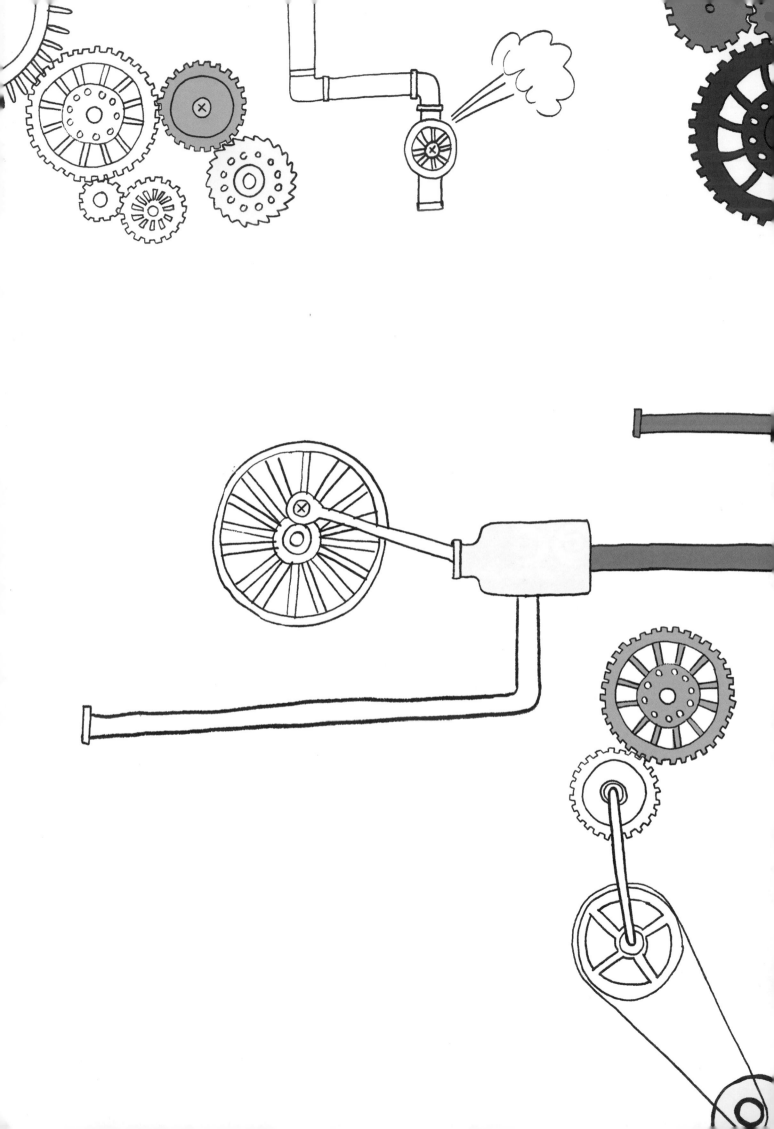

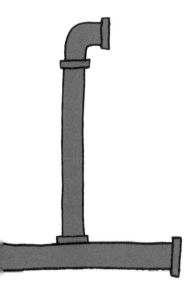

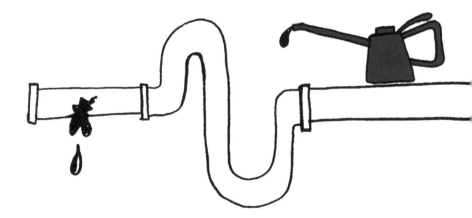

Connect the bits and bobs with pipes, cogs and wheels.

What is lurking underground?

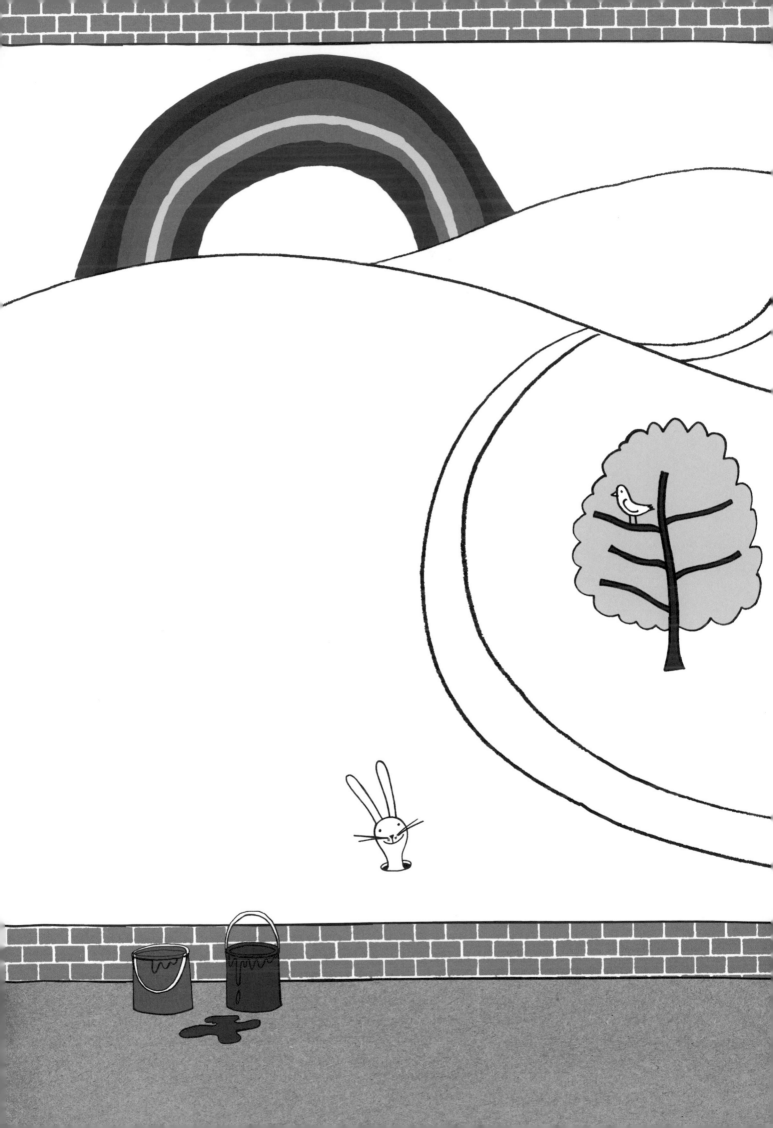

Complete the mural.

Draw more diggers and
lifters on the building site.

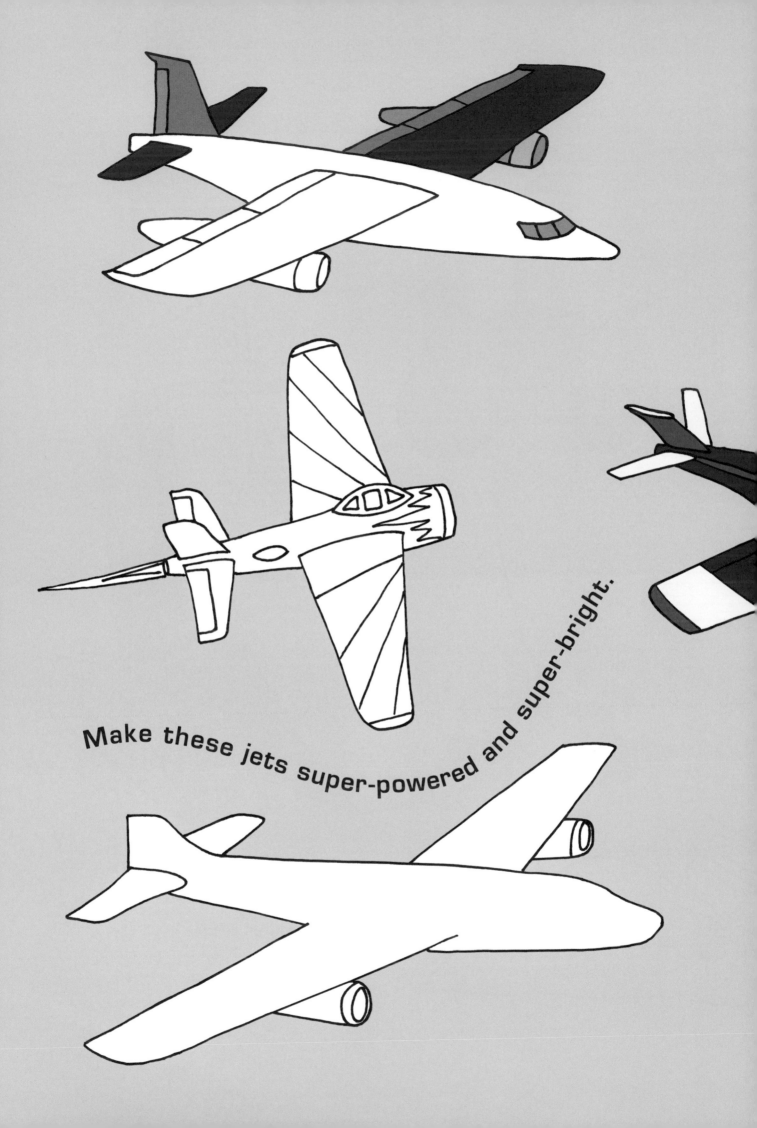

Make these jets super-powered and super-bright.

What is in the way of the toboggans?

Complete these creepy underwater creatures and add your own.

Finish the designs on the totem poles.

Cover these pages in trophies and sports gear.

Make your own weird and wonderful works of art.

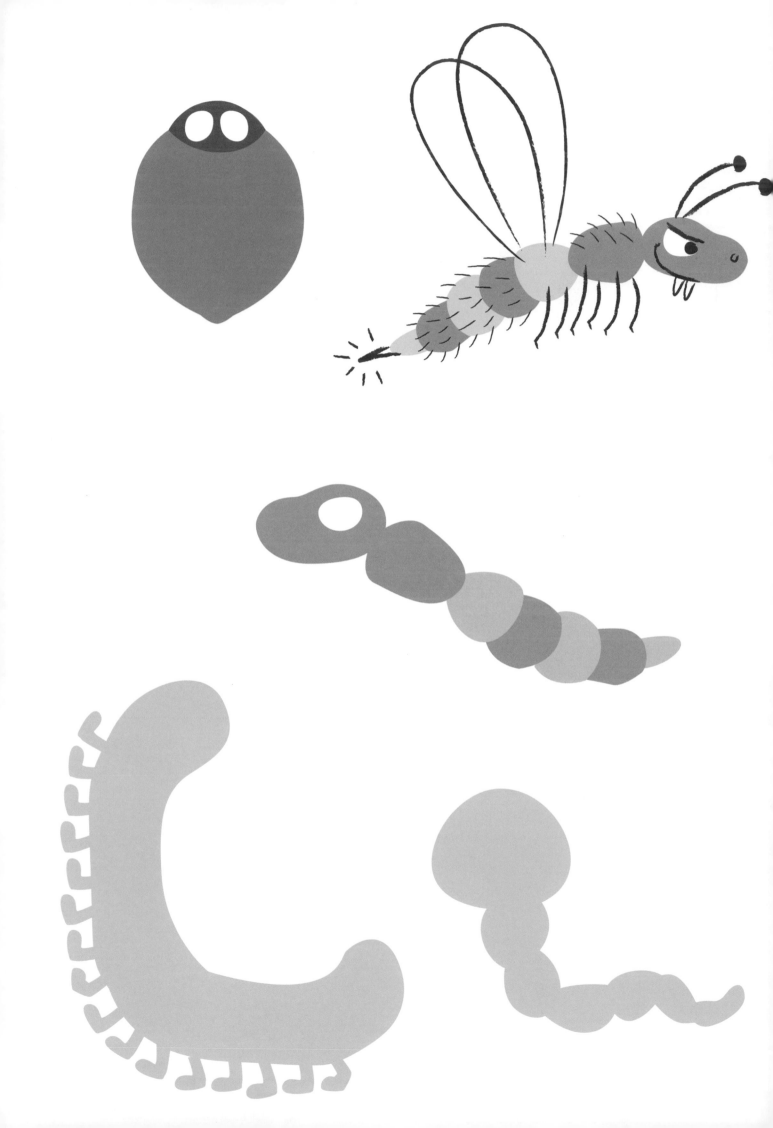

Give these icky insects your own finishing touches.

Super safari.

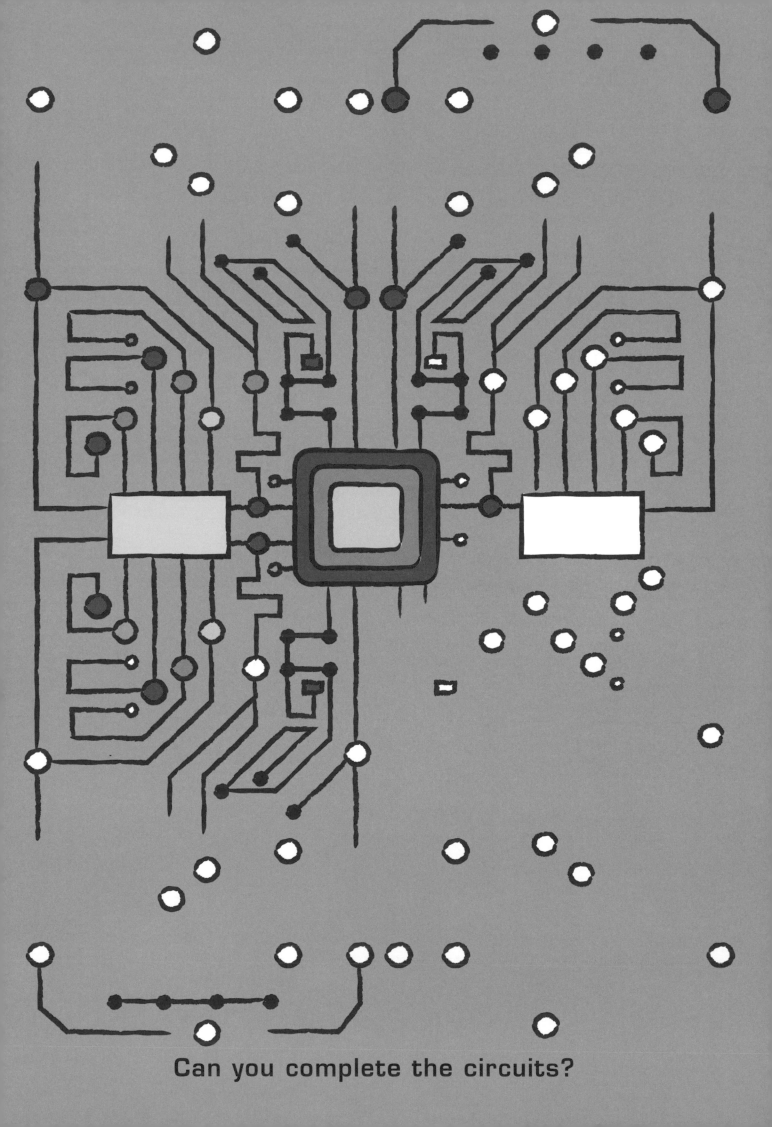

Can you complete the circuits?

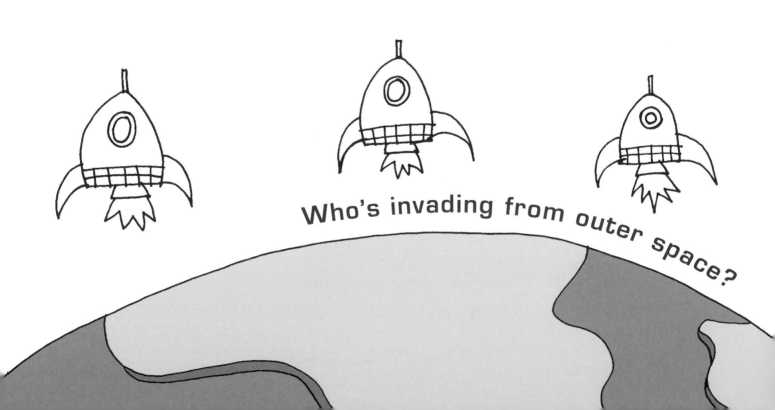

Who's invading from outer space?

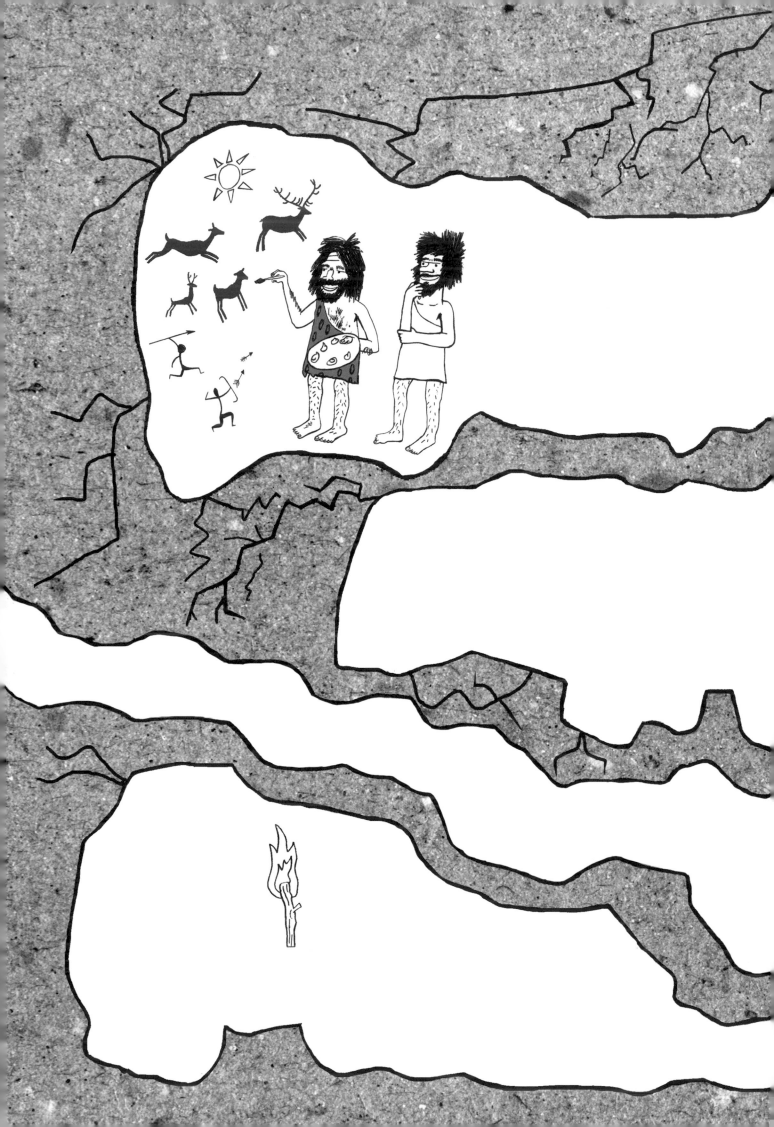

Fill the caves with paintings.

Make each planet into a world of your own.

What's happening in the town today?

Who is arriving at
Space City?

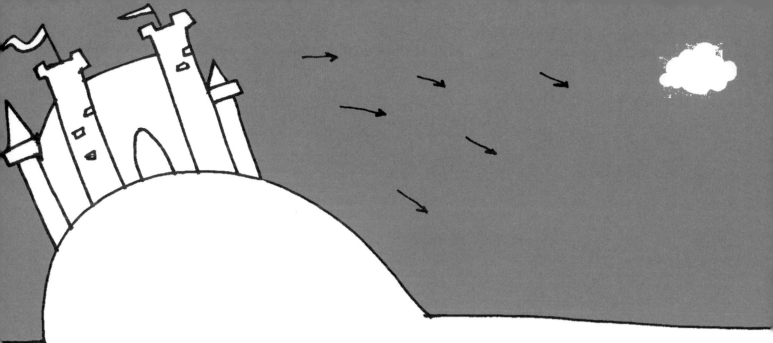

Fill the field with knights in armour.

Complete your own Aztec sun disk.

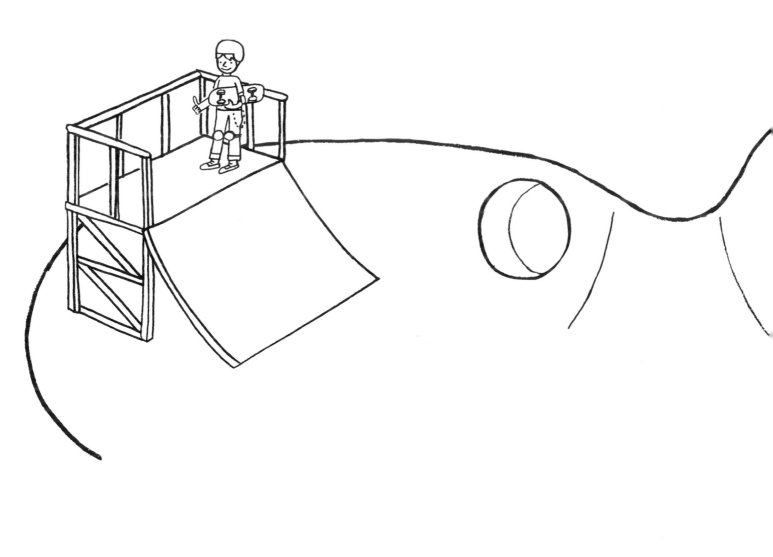

Make this skate park as cool as you can.

Turn these splats and splotches
into creepy creatures and
crawling critters.

More rockets!

Finish these funky badges.

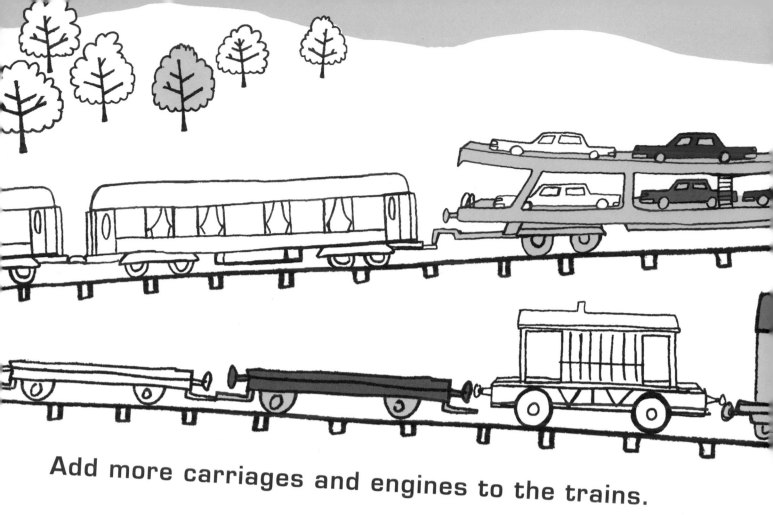

Add more carriages and engines to the trains.

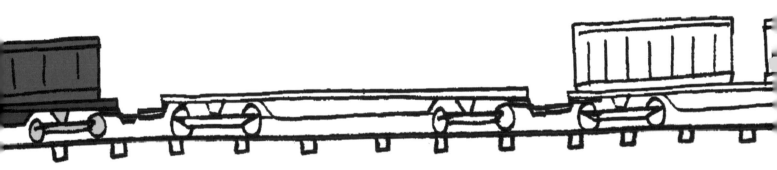

Add the finishing touches to this jungle scene.

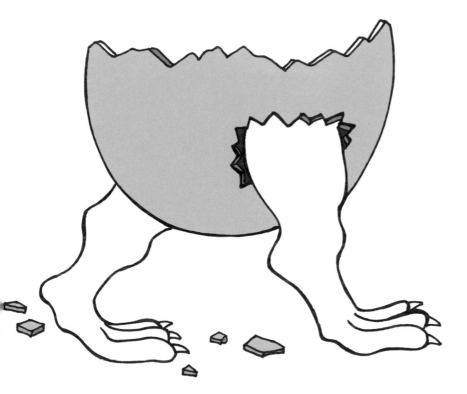

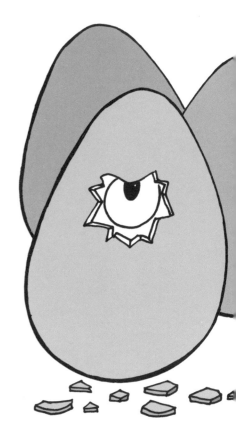

What is hatching from these eggs?

What weird creatures are lurking under the ocean?

More magnificent men in their flying machines.

Finish these funny faces.

Complete the medieval castle.

Customize your guitars ready for the band.

Add your own prehistoric monster.

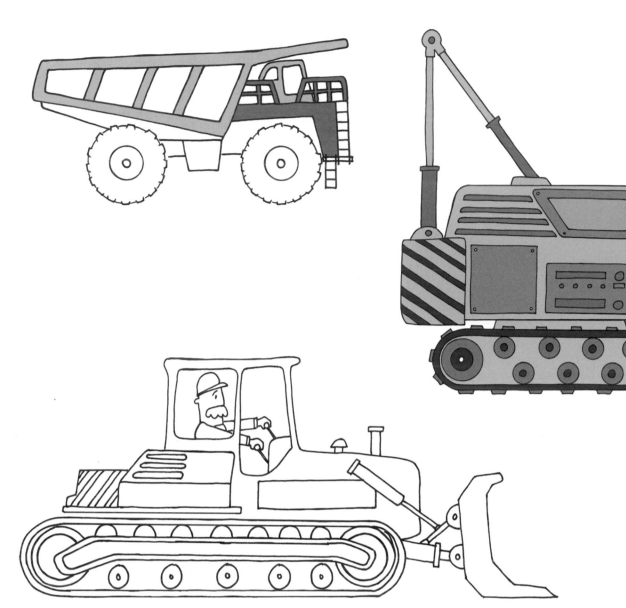

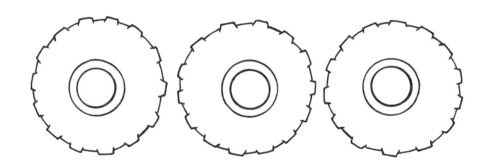

Complete this set of diggers and bulldozers.

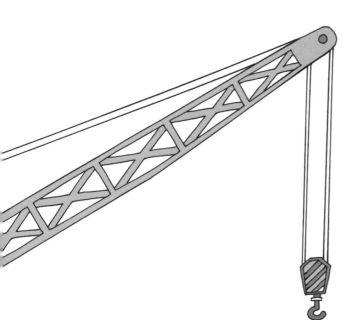

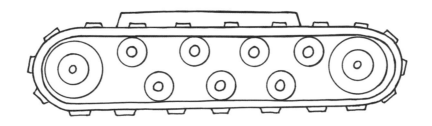

Yuck! What is skulking in the sewers?

Cover these pages in tools.

Customize these cool trainers.

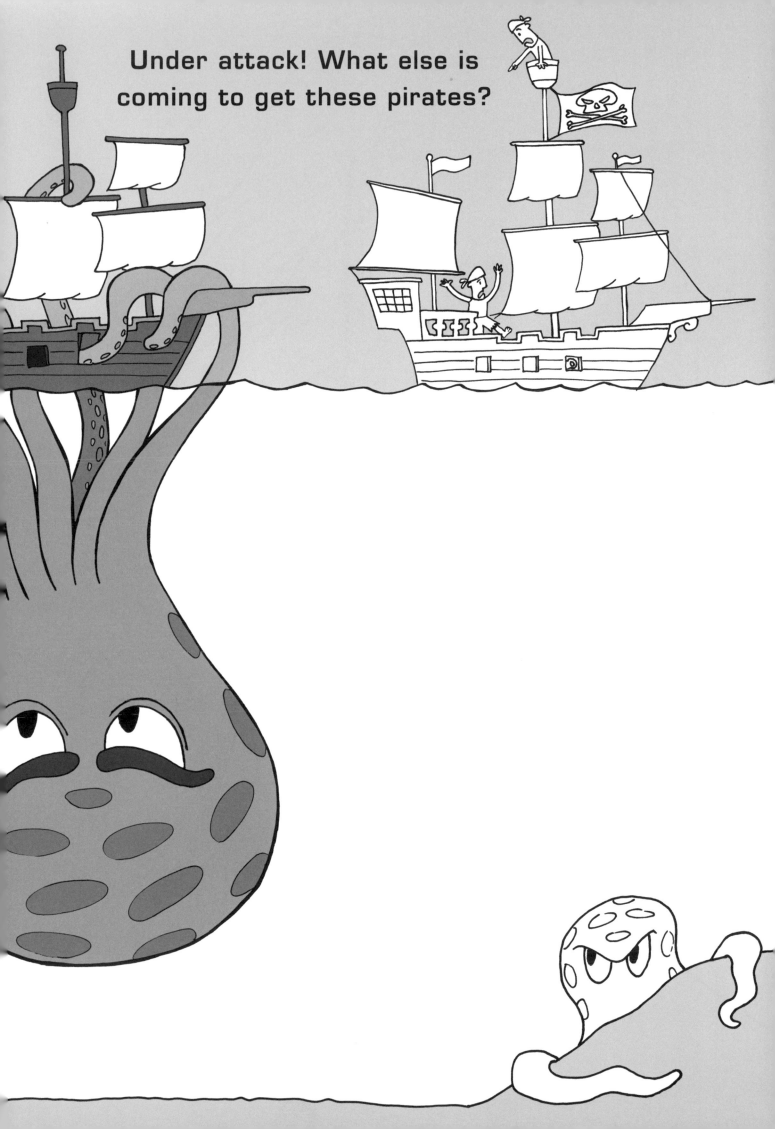

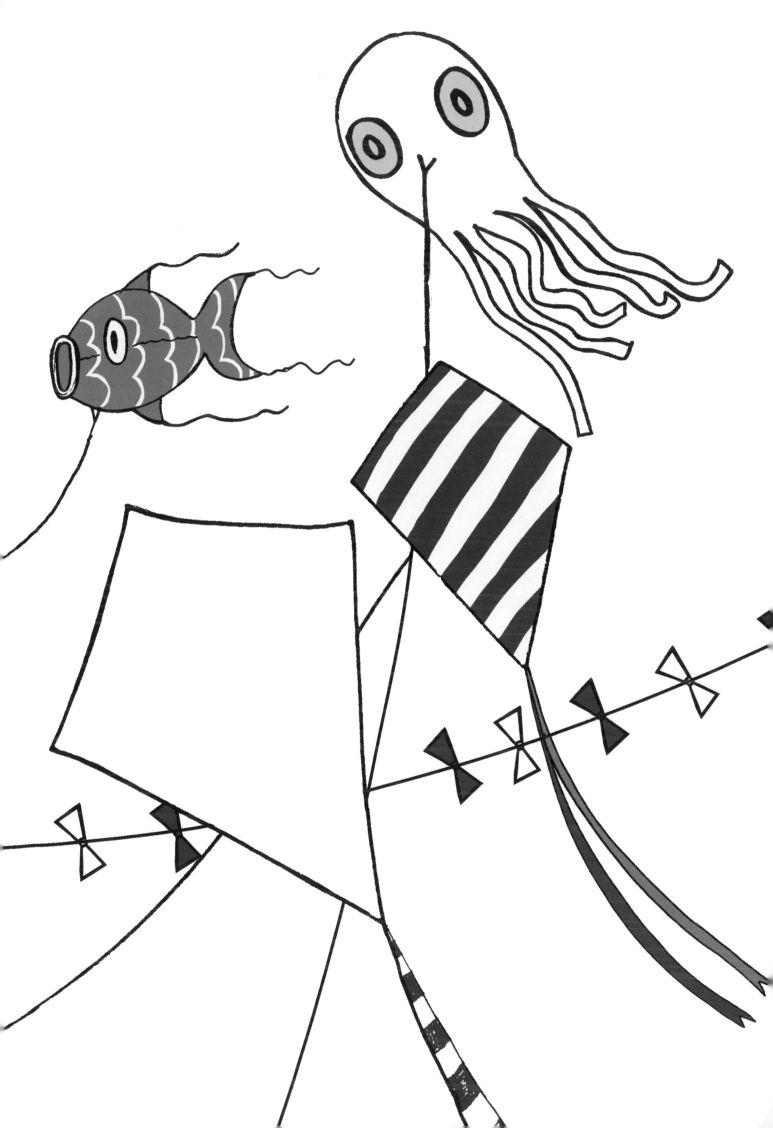

Kite fight! Finish the battle in the sky.

What lies in wait for the cave explorer?

Add spots, stripes, splotches and splodges to finish the safari scene.

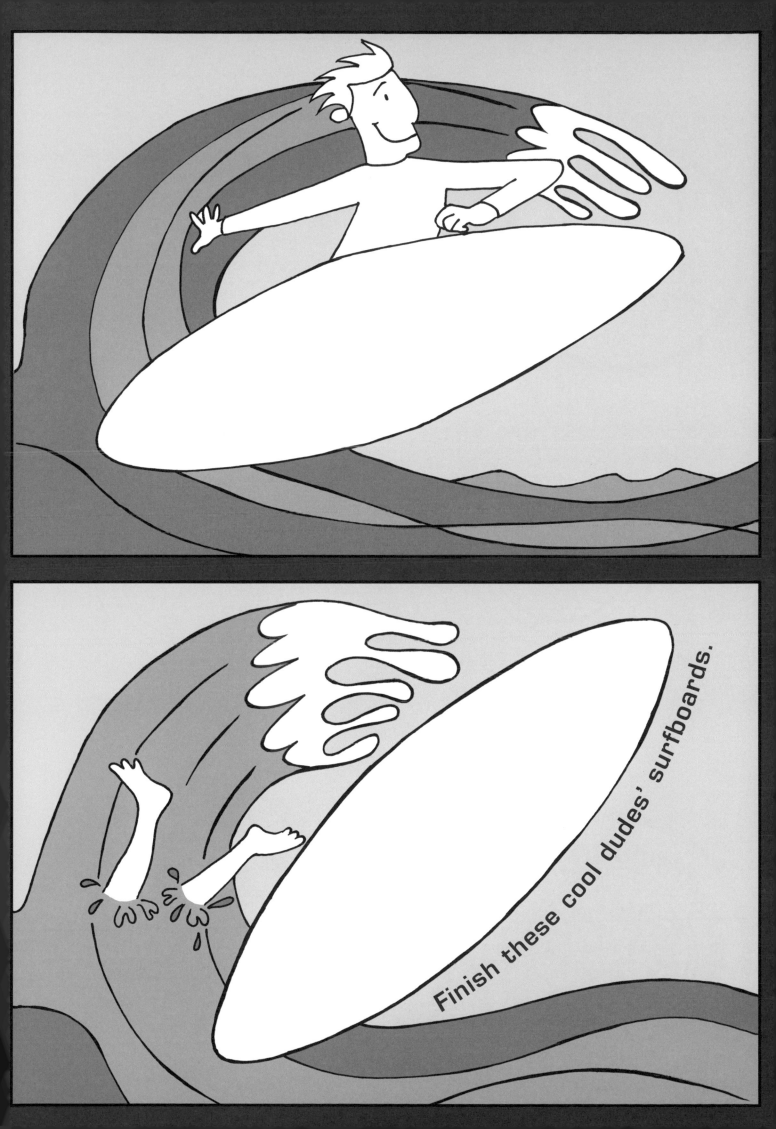

Finish these cool dudes' surfboards.

Give these bikes your own style.

Complete the fighting dragons and add your own.

Cool boards!

Complete these wacky, wheely, wobbly robots.

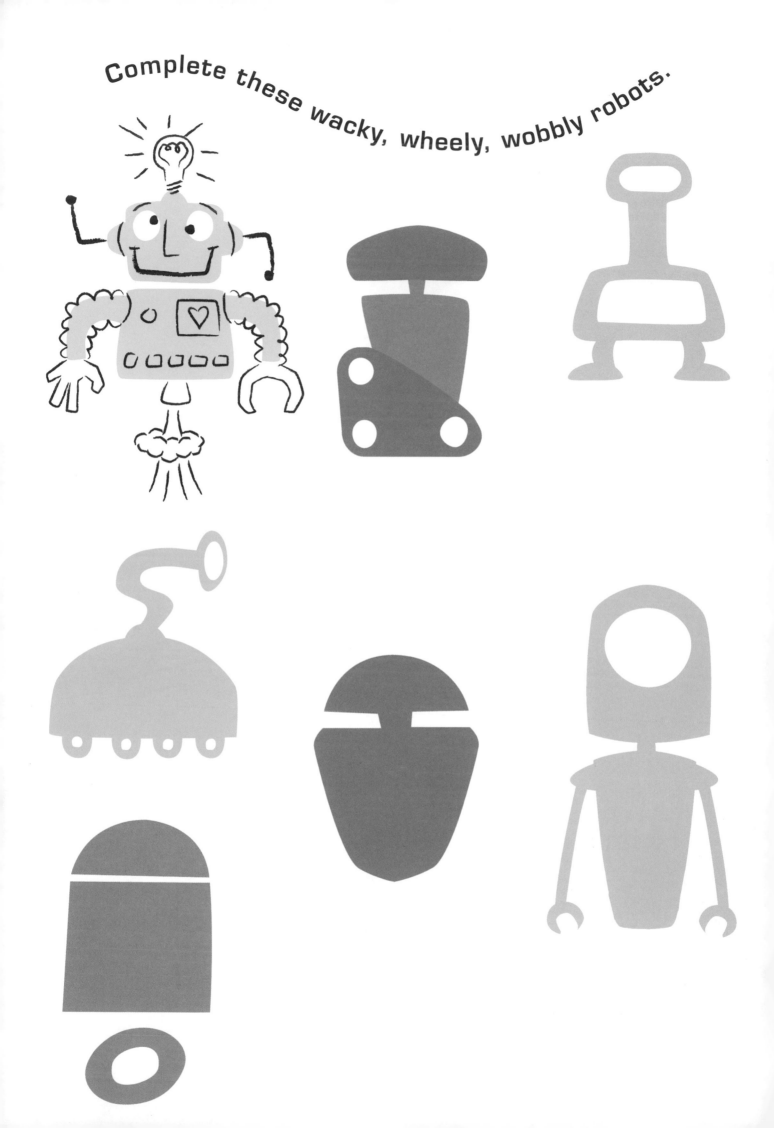

Complete the network of pipes.